5 May – I slept for a long time and, when I awoke, a dark castle loomed over us high in the mountains. The coach came to a halt and I waited anxiously outside the door. Finally, an old man dressed entirely in black opened it.

"Count Dracula?" I asked nervously.

"I am Dracula, and I bid you welcome to my house, Mr Harker." He bowed low before grasping my hand. His grip was strong and as cold as ice, making me flinch away.

Dracula sat with me while I ate, explaining that he had dined earlier. I looked at him carefully. Tall and old, he had a white moustache, bushy eyebrows beneath a domed forehead, and a long nose. His skin was exceptionally pale, and his ears pointed. I noticed the cruel set of his mouth and the very sharp canine teeth that lay over his lips. Oddly, his fingernails were cut to sharp points and he had hair growing on the palms of his hands. When he put his hand over mine, I shrank from his touch, and he smiled coldly. But, despite his unusual appearance, the count was fascinating and we talked until dawn.

The next day, Dracula did not appear until dark. I thought this strange, as he had summoned me here to make arrangements for the house, Carfax, that he is buying in England and there was much to discuss. I sat reading until he eventually came to find me. Then, again, we talked until the first light of morning.

CLASSIC COLLECTION

DRACULA

BRAM STOKER

ADAPTED BY ANNE ROONEY · ILLUSTRATED BY MIKE LOVE

Transylvania

Jonathan Harker's Diary

4 May – My train was late and it was already dark when I arrived at my room in the Hotel Krone in Transylvania, booked for me by Count Dracula. I asked the landlord if he could tell me anything about Dracula, who I had never met, but he made the sign of the cross and would say nothing. As I prepared to leave for Castle Dracula the next morning, the landlord's wife hung a large crucifix around my neck.

"If you really must go, take this for your mother's sake!" she whispered.

I am fearful of this visit for reasons I do not yet understand. If I do not make it home and this diary reaches my beloved Mina, let it be my goodbye to her...

On the coach, I picked out words such as 'devil' and 'vampire' from the other passengers' whispered conversations about me. It was an unpleasant start to the journey, but I tried to shake my feelings of unease and lose myself in the beauty of the scenery.

The coachman drove quickly, arriving early at the place where Dracula had arranged for his coach to pick me up.

"There is no coach here. Let's go," he said fearfully.

But, just then, a coach pulled by four coal-black horses arrived. Anxiously, I climbed on board. We rode for many hours. At times, the coachman, whose eyes glinted red, got down to scare away the howling wolves that followed us as we drove into the night.

Trapped

8 May – How I wish that I could leave this strange place! I am starting to feel ill at ease and afraid. I am sure the Count lives here alone – I never see any servants. As I was shaving this morning, he came up behind me in my room and laid a hand on my shoulder.

"Good Morning, Mr Harker," he breathed.

I had not seen his reflection approaching in the mirror. I jumped in shock and cut myself a little with the razor. When he saw the blood trickle down my chin, his eyes blazed and he made to grab my throat – but as he touched the beads of the crucifix around my neck, he snatched his hand back. I looked into the mirror again. He really did have no reflection! Seeing me look, he picked up the mirror and threw it out of the window. I suddenly remembered the fear of everyone I had met on the way here and their warnings, and felt grateful for the crucifix.

I went down to breakfast, still trembling. After eating alone (I have not yet seen Dracula eat) I decided to explore. Dracula's home stands on the edge of a sheer drop of a thousand feet, and I found locked doors every way I turned. The thought of being trapped here filled me with panic, and I ran frantically around the castle looking for an escape, but there was no way out. Castle Dracula is a prison and I am its prisoner!

12 May – This evening, I went for a walk around the castle. I am trapped here, but it gives me a sense of freedom to look through the large windows at the mountains. I noticed a light below me and, looking down, I saw the Count's head coming out of a window. As I watched, the rest of his body followed and he crept down the wall, face first, towards the yawning void below, with his black cape flowing behind him. I nearly shouted out in terror! What kind of a creature is he? I can feel the horror of this frightful place overpowering me.

16 May – Once again, I saw Dracula climb down the wall, then disappear. With him gone, I went to explore the castle and found a long-forgotten, dusty room. Feeling suddenly tired, I fell asleep there. Then, in the moonlight, I saw specks dancing before me. The specks formed into solid shapes, and I saw three women standing over me. Was I dreaming? They argued about who should kiss me first. All three had ruby-red lips and white shining teeth that filled me with both fear and a kind of longing. As one lowered her mouth to my neck, I felt her lips and teeth gently press against my throat.

Suddenly, the Count was in the room, his eyes bright red and blazing with anger.

"How dare you touch him!" he hissed. "You may have him when I am done with him." The women faded away, and I passed out.

Crates of Earth

18 May – I woke up in my own bed. When I went back to the room again, it was bolted from the inside. It had been no dream...

19 May – I am certainly in trouble. The Count insisted I write three letters, with future dates on them saying I was leaving or had already left the castle. I dared not argue. I am entirely at Dracula's mercy.

28 May – A band of gypsies have arrived and are working in the courtyard below my window. I wrote letters asking for help to my employer and to Mina, and bribed the gypsies to post them. But, this evening, Dracula brought the letters back to me in a foul temper.

17 June – More men arrived today, delivering big wooden crates with rope handles. I called out to the men for help, but they paid me no attention. They unloaded fifty crates.

25 June – Fear was making me desperate. I needed to escape. I climbed down the castle wall to the Count's empty room. I opened a heavy door and walked down a steep staircase that led to a ruined chapel. The roof of the chapel was coming down and the room smelled old and musty. The fifty crates from the courtyard stood full of newly dug earth. To my horror, I found the Count lying in one of them! He lay quite still, but his open eyes stared at me. I ran away in terror – I am sure I am going to meet my death here.

Leaving the Castle

29 June – The Count said I can leave the castle tomorrow. I begged to go today, but when he opened the door, a pack of wolves were snarling and blocking my path to freedom. I had no choice but to stay.

Much later, I heard whispering at my door, and then the Count saying quietly, "Be patient! Tomorrow night he will be yours!"

In the morning, the main door was locked again. Frantic, I made my way to the chapel. Dracula lay in his crate of earth, but a terrible change had come over him. He looked as though he had been given back his youth. His white hair was dark, his usually pale skin was flushed and his mouth was smeared with fresh blood. He lay still, like a fat, blood-filled leech. I realized that by helping him buy Carfax I have become part of his plan to terrorize London. The thought drove me mad. I seized a shovel and went to strike off his head. Suddenly, his head turned towards me and his eyes opened. I missed, but the shovel made a deep gash in the count's forehead before the lid of the crate crashed down.

I fled to my room and listened as the gypsies took Dracula and the crates of earth away. I was left alone in the castle, waiting for those terrible women to drain my blood. I shall scale the walls and face the wolves.

I will not wait here to die.

Whitby

Letter from Lucy Westenra to Mina Murray

24 May — My dear Mina, I must tell you a secret. I have had three proposals of marriage in one day! It upset me to have to disappoint two of the men, though. The first proposal was from Dr Seward, who keeps the lunatic asylum. The second was from Quincey Morris. I don't need to tell you that I said 'yes' to the third proposal from Arthur Holmwood! I cannot wait to marry my sweetheart!

Dr Seward's Diary

18 June – I bury myself in work to forget my sorrow over Lucy rejecting me. My patient, Renfield, becomes ever more interesting. Each day he catches flies, which he feeds to spiders he keeps in his cell.

1 July - I told Renfield to get rid of his 'pets'. He disgusted me by picking up a large fly and eating it. Now he has tamed a whole flock of sparrows, which he feeds with spiders, and asked me for a kitten! I refused.

20 July - Renfield said his sparrows had flown away, but the warden told me later that Renfield had been sick, bringing up a great mess of feathers and blood.

Mina's Diary

24 July – It is lovely here in Whitby. Lucy and I walk on the cliffs and sit on an old tombstone overlooking the bay. But I am worried as I have not heard from Jonathan on his visit to the Count. I wonder if he is thinking of me?

A terrible storm has struck the coast near Whitby. A ship tossed dangerously on the waves and looked certain to be lost but, by some miracle, was carried safely to shore. The mystery only deepened when we found no crew aboard – only a huge black dog, which quickly vanished, and the captain, dead and lashed with rope to the wheel. He had on him a letter that told a chilling tale of the crew being terrified by strange events and disappearing one by one at night. Some of them claimed to have seen a strange tall man. The cargo, a number of large crates of earth, was signed over to an unknown solicitor who took them away to London.

Mina's Diary

11 August – Still no news from Jonathan, and Lucy is sleepwalking. I woke in the night to find her gone from our room. I finally spotted her sitting on the old tombstone on the cliff, with a dark figure bending over her – a figure with a white face and gleaming red eyes. I ran to her, but when I reached her, she was alone. I pinned a shawl around her and brought her home where she slept for a long time. I noticed two small holes on her throat – I must have pricked her with the shawl pin.

13 August – For two nights, Lucy has been restless. Last night I woke to find her staring at the window where a large bat flapped about outside.

14 August – Coming home late last night after my stroll, I saw Lucy through our bedroom window and something that resembled a large bird next to her. But, she was back in bed when I got in. She is so pale and weak these days.

17 August – It is a miserable time. Lucy becomes more tired, her mother is also unwell, and there is still no news of Jonathan. At night Lucy gasps for air, and by day she is as weak as water. The wound on her throat is no better.

19 August – At last, news of Jonathan! He is in hospital in Budapest. The nurses do not know what happened to him and he has no memory of how he got there. I am going immediately to bring him home.

Dr Seward's Diary
19 August - Renfield is acting strangely. He escaped and I found him in the ruined house next to the asylum, called Carfax. We brought him back, but heard him murmuring, "I shall be patient, Master."

23 August - For three days, Renfield has been violent by day and quiet all night. Again he escaped, and went to Carfax. He was furious when we brought him back.

Lucy's Diary
25 August — My fiancé Arthur is worried for me, and mother's heart is ever more weak. My face is ghastly pale and my throat hurts. I am having terrible dreams.

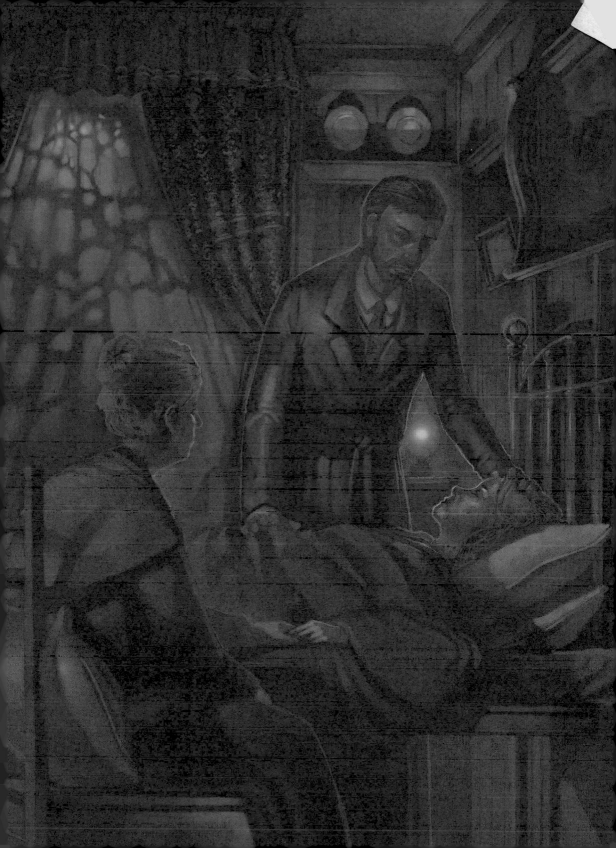

Blood and Garlic

Letter from Arthur Holmwood to Dr Seward
31 August – Dear Jack, I need a favour. Lucy is ill.
Will you come to Whitby and examine her, please?

Letter from Dr Seward to Arthur Holmwood
3 September - Dear Arthur, I went to see Lucy. She
had lost blood, but I could find no cause. I called
Professor Van Helsing over from Amsterdam. He
specializes in unexplained illnesses, but he could find
no sickness either.

Telegram from Dr Seward to Professor Van Helsing
6 September - Patient much worse. Come immediately.

Dr Seward's Diary
7 September - Van Helsing was shocked by the change in
Lucy. He said she needed a blood transfusion to save her
life. Her fiancé, Arthur, volunteered his own blood. Van
Helsing and I both think the wounds in Lucy's neck seem
much too small to have cost her all the blood she has lost.
He said I must watch Lucy constantly, and that he would
go back to Amsterdam to fetch his books to do more
research on the matter.

10 September - Lucy seemed much stronger the next day.
That night, I fell asleep outside her room. I woke in the
morning to find Van Helsing back. Lucy was worse than
ever, her lips drained white. We began another transfusion,
using my own blood, and managed to keep her alive.

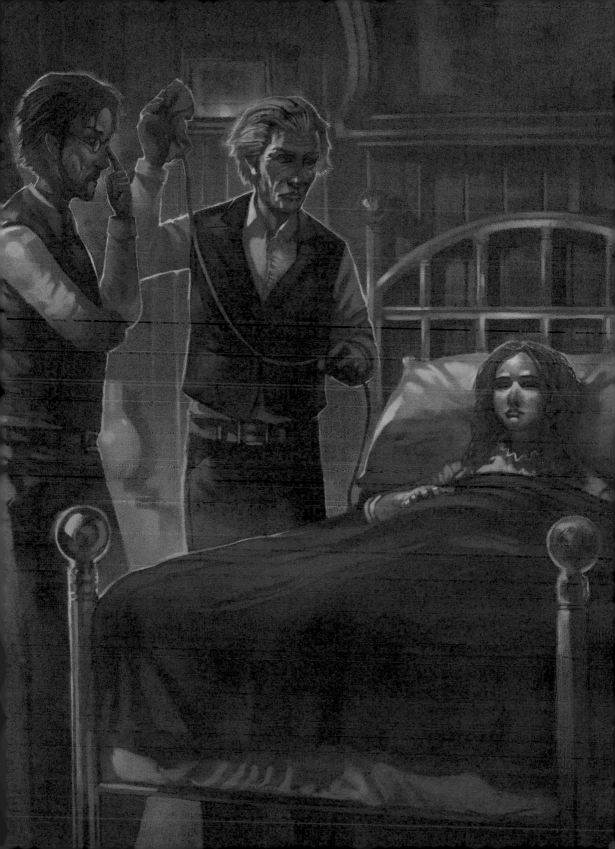

13 September - Yesterday, Van Helsing filled Lucy's room with white garlic flowers and hung more around her neck. He says they will ward off evil. He made Lucy promise not to move them. But, this morning, Lucy's mother told us that she had found the sickly smelling flowers and removed them whilst Lucy was asleep.

When she had gone, Van Helsing broke down in despair.

"What has she done! This mother, all unknowing, may have caused the loss of her daughter, body and soul!"

Lucy looked even worse than before. This time, I took blood from Van Helsing to give to her.

Lucy's Diary

17 September — Four days of peace! I have woken today feeling much better. Under Professor Van Helsing's care, I have been able to sleep without fear of horrible dreams.

Dr Seward's Diary

17 September - This evening, Renfield burst into my room. He lunged at me with a knife, cutting my wrist. When I looked up from binding my cut, I saw that he was on the floor lapping up the spilled blood like a dog!

Note by Lucy Westenra

17 September — I write this as a record should anything happen to me. After the events of tonight, I feel on the brink of death: I couldn't sleep, a bat was beating against the window, and something howled outside. Mother came to my bed, frightened by the noises.

22

Suddenly, the window smashed and a wolf poked its head in. Horrified, Mother collapsed. Her hand got caught in the flowers around my neck as she fell, ripping them away. The room spun, then filled with tiny specks that formed the shape of three beautiful ladies, before everything went dark. When I woke again, I saw my poor mother, dead from the shock. I was alone with her body, and I laid my white flowers over her. The wolf is still howling outside, and the specks continue to dance.

Dr Seward's Diary

18 September - Van Helsing and I went straight to Lucy's room this morning. Two women lay on the bed: Mrs Westenra dead, and Lucy almost so. Even another blood transfusion, this time from Quincey Morris, did not work. She awoke long enough to realize her mother had died, then slept. Her gums had shrunk further and her teeth looked longer and sharper than before. When Van Helsing came to check on her, he gasped. The wounds on her neck were completely healed.

"She's dying!" he exclaimed. "It won't be long."

We called Arthur in, and Lucy opened her eyes and spoke in a voice I'd never heard from her before.

"Arthur! Oh, my love! Kiss me!"

But Van Helsing wouldn't let him. A look of rage crossed Lucy's face. Soon after, she closed her eyes forever.

"At least there is peace for her now," I said sadly.

"Alas, no!" Van Helsing said. "It is only the beginning."

The Count Returns

Mina's Diary

22 September – Jonathan and I have returned from Budapest to England, happily married. While walking through London, Jonathan stopped and stared at a man with a cruel face, a dark moustache and long, sharp teeth.

"Heaven help us!" he said. "The Count, grown young!"

I worry about what happened to Jonathan during his time in Transylvania but I dare not ask.

25 September – Van Helsing visited me, and I let him read Jonathan's diary. I was afraid he would think dear Jonathan mad, but he believes all Jonathan has written to be true.

Dr Seward's Diary

26 September - Van Helsing showed me this report:

Westminster Gazette   **26 September**
   Over the last few days, there have been reports of young children being lured away by a strange lady. Some have two small wounds on the throat, as if bitten by a dog or rat.

Van Helsing says the children's wounds have been made by Lucy! Worse - he wanted me to go with him to open her tomb. Once we got there, he forced open the lid of the coffin. Lucy was gone! After a while, I saw a white shape between the trees. The professor ran over and returned carrying a child. We left the child in a safe place and went home.

I still could not believe this was Lucy's work.

27 September - We went to Lucy's tomb again; her body had returned. Van Helsing drew back her lips to show me her long pointed teeth. He revealed that Lucy had been bitten by a vampire and that she is now a vampire herself! To set her soul free we must - horror of all horrors - drive a stake through her heart and cut off her head!

Van Helsing is going alone tonight to seal Lucy's tomb with garlic and a crucifix, to try to stop her leaving it. By tomorrow night, she will be desperate for blood.

29 September - Van Helsing told Arthur and Quincey about his plan.

"Not for the whole world!" cried Arthur.

However, we managed to persuade him to come. But when we opened the coffin, it was empty once more. Van Helsing sealed the empty tomb with putty mixed with holy wafers to prevent Lucy entering. At last, her pale figure appeared, carrying a young victim. Arthur gasped at the blood dripping from her mouth. Lucy snarled, her eyes burning red with fury. She put down the child, then held out her arms to Arthur.

"Come to me, my love! We shall rest together!"

As Arthur stepped towards her, Van Helsing sprang forward with a crucifix. Lucy shrank back, turning to her tomb. But the putty prevented her getting in.

When Arthur finally agreed that we could carry out Van Helsing's plan, Van Helsing removed the seal and allowed Lucy to slip into her tomb.

"We can do no more tonight," he said.

Dr Seward's Diary

28 September - Today, we went to open Lucy's tomb again. Van Helsing explained that if Lucy remained as she was, the people she killed would also become vampires. Arthur agreed to set Lucy's spirit free as an act of love. He held a sharpened wooden stake over Lucy's heart and struck it with a hammer. She screeched as blood spurted from the wound. But Arthur carried on until she was still. In death, her face grew peaceful and beautiful again.

29 September - Van Helsing invited Jonathan and his wife, Mina, to join us. They have important information.

30 September - I know now that the house Renfield goes to is Carfax, the Count's new lair!

Mina's Diary

30 September – "There are such beings as vampires," Van Helsing told us. "The Count is one. He can take different shapes, such as a dog, wolf or bat. He can command the weather. He has the strength of many men and throws no reflection. He can't bear garlic or anything holy. He comes alive by night, but by day he must lie in special earth.

"Vampires do not age. They do not eat, but drink the blood of others and grow stronger. Dracula will turn us into the cursed undead, unless we kill him first. He had fifty crates of earth sent to London and Carfax. We must find them as they are the only places he can safely sleep during the day."

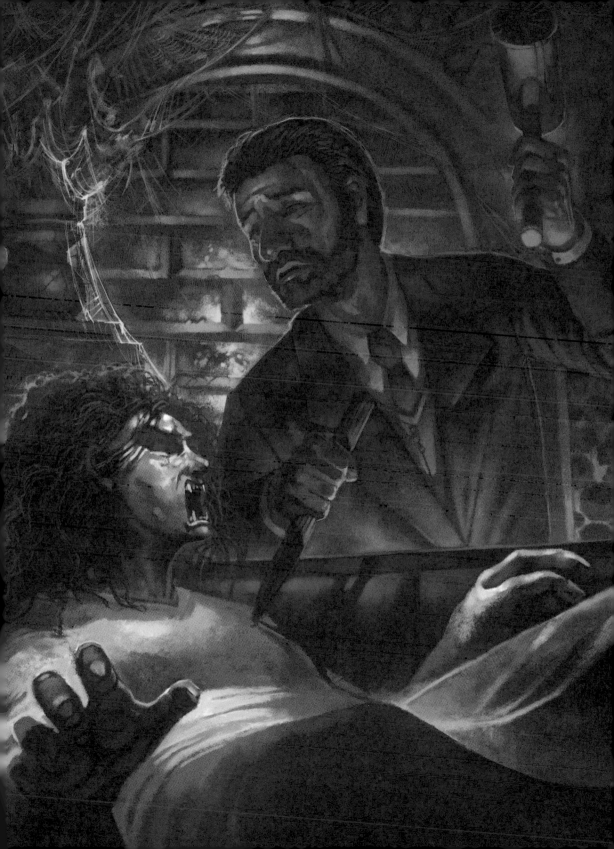

Renfield

Jonathan Harker's Diary

1 October – Van Helsing made sure we were armed against physical and spiritual danger before we entered Carfax. The whole place was thick with dust. We found the chapel, which stank of earth and stale blood, and counted the crates. There were twenty-nine, so Dracula must already have moved the others.

When I returned to Seward's asylum, where we have a room, Mina was sleeping soundly. She looked pale and all the adventure is tiring her. It was difficult to rouse her.

I tracked down the men the Count had employed to move his crates of earth and have discovered their location – nine have gone to a house in Piccadilly, the rest to other houses in London.

Dr Seward's Diary

3 October - I found Renfield lying in a pool of blood in his cell in the early hours. He was still alive, but his face had been smashed up and his back was broken. I called for Arthur, Van Helsing and Quincey. Renfield had clearly been under Dracula's spell all along. He managed to tell us that the Count had come to him two nights ago and promised him new victims - not just flies, but rats and better. The following day, Mina had visited Renfield, but she was pale and weak. When the Count next came, Renfield asked him what he had done to Mina. The Count was furious and threw Renfield to the floor - that was where we found him.

Full of dread, we went to the Harkers' room.
The door was locked and Van Helsing forced it open.
Jonathan was asleep, but Mina knelt by the window, a
dark figure stooping over her. He held her face against
his chest where a thin stream of blood trickled to her
mouth. At our appearance, the Count sprang back.
Van Helsing held up his holy wafers and we held out
our crucifixes and for a moment the Count was
frozen, fury burning in his red, glowing eyes. Then a
cloud covered the moon, and when light filled the
room again, we saw only a mist disappearing under the
door - Dracula was gone.

At the same moment, Mina let out a piercing
scream and Jonathan awoke. Van Helsing encouraged
Mina to tell us what had happened.

"I felt the presence of someone in the room, and
immediately tried to wake Jonathan, but he was too
soundly asleep. Then the Count appeared next to me -
I recognized him from your descriptions. He said that
if I woke Jonathan he would dash out his brains.
Then he put his foul mouth to my neck and I felt my
strength falling away. After that, he pushed my face
against his chest and said that I would forever be his.
Oh, what has become of me?"

Arthur and Quincey went to look for any
sign of the Count. They found my room
ransacked, and Renfield dead, but the
Count had gone. Outside the window,
the silhouette of a great bat flitted
through the night sky.

Driving Out the Count

Jonathan Harker's Diary

3 October – Following the terrible events, we made our plans. Before we left, Van Helsing tried to protect Mina by touching her forehead with a holy wafer. She screamed in pain. The wafer left a cruel red scar on her skin, but it was not as painful as the realization of what it meant – that she was already becoming one of Dracula's kind.

We went first to Carfax. Nothing had been disturbed. We opened each of the crates and placed a holy wafer inside, making them unusable by the Count. Then we took a train to London. The smell in the Piccadilly house was vile. We found only eight of the nine crates that had been delivered there – so one was missing. We put holy wafers in all eight. The keys for the Count's other London houses were there, too, so Arthur and Quincey set off to destroy the remaining crates.

Dr Seward's Diary

3 October - Our work done, we waited in the Piccadilly house for Dracula's return. Jonathan was prepared with a long knife. When the Count appeared, Jonathan leapt at him, but he was too quick, and the knife only cut his coat. We held up our crucifixes.

"You will be sorry," Dracula snarled evilly. "My revenge has only just begun. It will spread over centuries!"

He threw himself through a window, scattering glass everywhere, and fled into the night.

In Pursuit

Jonathan Harker's Diary

3-4 October – Before dawn, Van Helsing hypnotized Mina to see if she could read the Count's mind...

"What can you see?" he asked

"Nothing – blackness."

"What can you hear?"

"Lapping water. A creaking chain. Men's footsteps."

"He's on a ship!" cried Van Helsing. "He's escaping back to Transylvania, travelling in his last crate of earth."

Mina's Diary

5 October – We have investigated all the ships sailing to Eastern Europe and have found the right one: the *Czarina Catherine*. It's sailing for the port of Varna, close to Castle Dracula. We need to get there overland before it arrives.

"We must find him," Van Helsing said. "He has contaminated you already, Mina. If he is not destroyed, when you die, you will become like him. If we let him live, he will survive centuries, making more of his type."

I feel peaceful tonight. But I know I am still unclean.

Dr Seward's Diary

11 October - We are going by train to Varna and will arrive before the Count. Van Helsing will hypnotize Mina each day, so she can tell us what the Count is doing. Mina made Jonathan promise that if she changes too much, he will kill her and free her spirit.

24 October - We travelled day and night and arrived in Varna a week ago. Dracula's ship has still not docked…

28 October - We received news that the *Czarina Catherine* has docked at Galatz instead. The Count must suspect we are following him and is taking a different route.

Jonathan Harker's Diary
30 October – We went to the port and spoke to the captain of the *Czarina Catherine*. The sailors had not liked the crate and wanted to throw it overboard. The captain stopped them, but one sailor had been found dead, with throat wounds as if torn apart by a wild animal.

Mina's Diary
30 October – I've consulted the maps and have worked out the Count's new route. We will intercept him. Arthur and Jonathan will get a boat to follow him. Dr Seward and Quincey will take horses and ride along the bank. Meanwhile, Van Helsing will take me overland to the Count's castle – we need to stay together so that he can hypnotize me. It was torture to say goodbye to Jonathan.

31 October – Van Helsing has paid for a carriage and we will set off tomorrow. I pray that we will stay safe.

2 November – We have driven all day. The countryside is beautiful, but it is so cold here. Hypnotized, I still hear water – the Count is definitely travelling by boat.

Castle Dracula

Note by Van Helsing

3 November – The sky is heavy with snow. Mina sleeps all the time and no longer eats. I could not hypnotize her today. I worry about her.

5 November – Still she sleeps all day and wakes by night. I struggle to stay awake with her. Tonight, we are in the shadow of Castle Dracula. At sunset, I built a fire and wrapped Mina in rugs. She is as pale as the snow. I drew a circle around us and crumbled the holy wafer all around its edge. When I suggested she step outside, she could not, so I know we are safe – if she can't leave the circle, those like her cannot enter it.

Late at night, the horses whinnied with fear. As the fire burned low, I saw shapes in the swirling snow – three women in long dresses. Mina would not let me leave the circle to rebuild the fire, but I said I needed to keep her warm and safe.

"I am safer from them than anyone!" she laughed. Looking at the scar burned into her forehead by the holy wafer, I knew it was true.

"Come to us, sister!" the vampires called, coming closer.

But they could not cross the circle and Mina could not leave it. The horses now lay still and I realized they were dead. The horror continued until dawn when the figures dissolved into the drifting snowflakes. Mina fell into another deep sleep.

Jonathan's Diary

4 November – An accident to our boat means we must now continue our journey by land. I wish Quincey and Seward were with us! I am afraid to return to the place that filled me with such terror and I am worried for the safety of my beloved Mina.

Dr Seward's Diary

5 November - At dawn we saw a band of gypsies riding from the river with a wagon carrying the crate of earth. The snow falls and the wolves howl. I fear that we are riding to the death of someone - I do not know who.

Note by Van Helsing

5 November – While Mina slept in the circle, I went to Castle Dracula and searched the chapel until I found the tombs of the three vampire women. Even I was nearly distracted by their beauty. But I shook off the feeling and continued my search. I found a grand, empty tomb labelled 'Dracula', and laid some of the holy wafer inside it. Then I turned to my terrible task. Oh, I trembled, and tremble still, to think of it. I heard the horrid screeching as I drove the stakes through the hearts of all three of the vampire women, one by one. It is over, and for a brief moment, each of their faces was finally at peace before their bodies crumbled to dust. In the distance I heard the sound of Mina's call and left the castle immediately to return to her.

The Last Crate

Mina's Diary

6 November – After a long wait, we saw the gypsies arriving with the last crate. It was a race against time. We knew that as soon as the sun went down, the creature in it would rise. The gypsies whipped their horses, racing to reach the castle before dark. Dr Seward and Quincey attacked from one direction and Jonathan and Arthur from the other.

The gypsies stopped and Jonathan and Quincey fought past them, but Quincey was badly hurt. Jonathan broke the crate open. The Count lay motionless inside, his red eyes glowing. Then, just as the last rays of sunlight faded, his body came to life and he raised his head triumphantly from the crate. His lips curled back in fury, fangs at the ready.

At that same moment, Jonathan sliced Dracula's throat with his knife and Quincey plunged his into Dracula's heart. In an instant, the vampire's body crumbled to dust and drifted away on the wind. It was over!

Quincey sank to the ground, blood gushing from his side. "The snow is as unstained as her forehead!" He pointed to me weakly, my scar gone, and he died with a smile. We wept.

Note by Jonathan Harker

Seven years on, Mina and I are happy and have a son, Quincey. We can only repeat Van Helsing's words on these events: "We ask no one to believe this wild story and are merely glad it is at an end."

About the author

Abraham 'Bram' Stoker was born in 1847 in Dublin, Ireland. Stoker was bedridden with an unknown illness until he started school at the age of seven, when he made a complete recovery. He grew up without further illness, and even excelled as an athlete while at Trinity College, Dublin. Stoker later became manager of The Lyceum Theatre in London for 27 years. This job allowed him to travel the world, giving him inspiration for his horror stories. After suffering a number of strokes, Stoker died in April 1912.

QED Project Editor: Tasha Percy
Editorial Director: Victoria Garrard
Art Director: Laura Roberts-Jensen
Editor: Louise John
Designer: Rachel Clark

Copyright © QED Publishing 2014

First published in the UK in 2014 by
QED Publishing, A Quarto Group company,
The Old Brewery, 6 Blundell Street, London, N7 9BH

www.qed-publishing.co.uk

A catalogue record for this book is available from the British Library.

ISBN 978 1 78171 631 1

Printed in China